A Tune A Day

FOR
Trombone *or* Euphonium.
(Baritone)
By C. Paul Herfurth.

Bass Clef Book One.

Thomas Colledge

Exclusive Distributors:
Music Sales Limited
8/9 Frith Street, London W1V 5TZ, England.
Music Sales Pty Limited
120 Rothschild Avenue, Rosebery, NSW 2018, Australia.

Order No. BM10256
ISBN 0.7119.1580.6

© *Boston Music Company*

Boston Music Company.

FOREWORD TO TEACHERS

IN compiling this course the objective has intentionally been not to cover too much ground; but rather to concentrate on the acquisition of a thorough musical background and a solid foundation in good trombone or euphonium (baritone) playing. These two requisites are inseparable.

A brief section is devoted to the simpler rudiments of music which should be thoroughly understood as the need arises.

The learning of the positions and fingerings as introduced should be insisted upon.

Cultivate in the pupil the habit of careful listening.

The familiar hymns and folk-songs have been selected because of their melodic interest as pieces, and because, in addition, in each appears some technical point to be mastered.

The value of learning to " think count" from the very beginning cannot be over-estimated. Only in this way can a pupil sense rhythm. Rhythm, one of the most essential elements of music, and usually conspicuous by its absence in amateur ensemble playing, is emphasized throughout.

Many teachers do the thinking for their pupils, instead of helping them to think for themselves. Insisting upon the mastery of each point will not dull their interest. What greater gratification can there be for a pupil, whether child or adult, than self-accomplishment in a set task?

Class teaching should be a combination of individual instruction and ensemble playing. At every lesson there should be individual playing so that all the necessary corrections can be made. Never allow pupils' mistakes to go unnoticed, since only by immediate correction will they develop the habit of careful thinking and playing.

A decided advantage of group-teaching is that it provides experience in ensemble playing and gives every pupil the opportunity of listening to the others, of observing their mistakes, and of profiting from the corrections.

For the best results each class should not be made up of more than six for a half-hour lesson, and twelve for an hour lesson. Irrespective of the numbers, the teacher must see to it that there is individual instruction as well as general class direction.

Classes should be regraded whenever necessary so as not to retard the progress of the more gifted students, or discourage the less musically endowed. This procedure also acts as an incentive for greater effort on the part of the pupils.

The lip slurs on page 32 should be used whenever necessary according to the individual student's requirements.

Eventual success in mastering the instrument depends on regular and careful application to its technical demands. Daily practice should not extend beyond the limits of the player's physical endurance—the aim should be the gradual development of lip and breath control alongside assured finger-work.

The material in this method is so written as to be usable with "A Tune A Day" for cornet or trumpet.

Pictures were posed by Fred Peterson (solo trombone), C. J. Scott, High School Band, East Orange, N. J.

C. PAUL HERFURTH
Director of Instrumental Music
East Orange, N. J.

RUDIMENTS OF MUSIC

Music is represented on paper by a combination of characters and signs, all of which it is necessary to learn in order to play the trombone or euphonium (baritone) intelligently.

Symbols called notes are written upon and between five lines, which is the staff.

The sign placed at the beginning of the staff is called the bass or F clef.

The staff is divided by barlines into bars as follows:

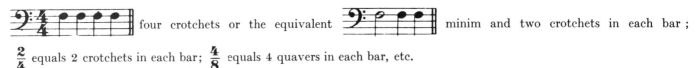

These bars, in turn, are equal in time value, according to the fractional numbers, (Time signature) placed at the beginning of the music.

The time signature indicates the number of notes of equal value in each bar. The upper figure gives the number of beats or counts in a bar, and the lower figure indicates what kind of a note has one beat. For example, $\frac{4}{4}$ or $\mathbf{C}$ equals

 four crotchets or the equivalent minim and two crotchets in each bar;

$\frac{2}{4}$ equals 2 crotchets in each bar; $\frac{4}{8}$ equals 4 quavers in each bar, etc.

There are different kinds of notes, each variety representing a certain time value as follows:

1 2 3 4   1 2 3 4   1 2 3 4   1 & 2 & 3 & 4 &

Semibreve equals: Two Minims, Four Crotchets, or Eight Quavers.

The count for the above would be, four to the semibreves; two to each minim; one to each crotchet and one to each group of two quavers.

The notes are named after the first seven letters of the alphabet, i.e., (a, b, c, d, e, f, g,) according to the line on, or space in which they are placed.

The Bass (F) clef which starts on the fourth line, establishes the note F on this line, from which the other lines and spaces are named as follows:

F   G   A   F   E   D   C   B   A   G

In addition notes are written upon and between short lines above and below the staff. These lines are called leger lines.

B   C   D   E   F   F   E

LINE NOTES   SPACE NOTES

Good Boys Deserve Favours Also   All Children Enjoy Goodies

A rest indicates a pause or silence for the value of the note after which it is named, such as:

Semibreve Rest   Minim Rests   Crotchet Rests   Quaver Rests

The end of the piece is indicated by a light and heavy line

When a section or part of a piece is to be repeated it will be shown by a double bar with two dots.

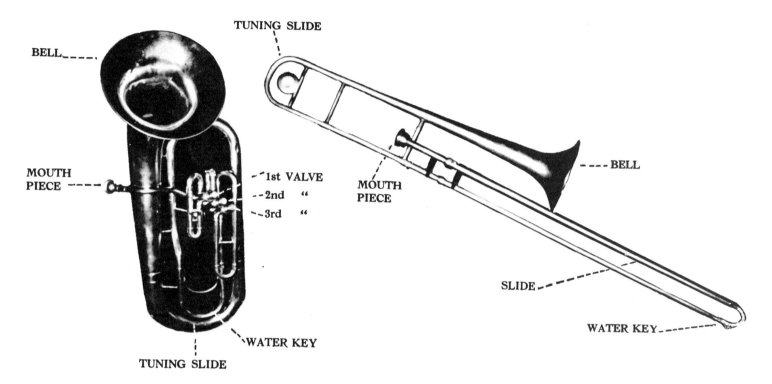

TO THE STUDENT

A clearer understanding of the construction and mechanics of the instrument you are about to play will prove most helpful in learning your positions (fingering).

When the 1st position (no valves) are sounded the shortest length of tubing is in use. By extending the slide (depressing the valves) additional tubing is opened, thereby lowering the pitch as follows:

The 2nd position (2nd valve) lowers the pitch of an open note by ONE-SEMITONE

The 3rd   ,,   (1st valve)   ,,   ,,   ,,   ,, ,,   ,,   ,,   ,,   ONE WHOLE TONE

The 4th   ,,   (3rd valve)   ,,   ,,   ,,   ,, ,,   ,,   ,,   ,,   ONE TONE AND A SEMITONE

The 5th   ,,   (2nd & 3rd, valve) lowers the pitch of an open note by TWO WHOLE TONES

The 6th   ,,   (1st & 3rd valve)   ,,   ,,   ,,   ,, ,,   ,,   ,,   ,,   TWO TONES AND A SEMITONE

The 7th   ,,   (All three valves)   ,,   ,,   ,,   ,, ,,   ,,   ,,   ,,   THREE WHOLE TONES

For the baritone student it is easy to see that the 1st and 2nd valves combined is equal to the 3rd valve. This 3rd valve however, is rarely used separately except in very rapid playing, as it is slightly out of tune.

TUNING YOUR INSTRUMENT

The trombone and baritone in the bass clef are treated as non-transposing instruments. That means they sound the actual pitch of the notes as they are written. Drawing out the tuning slide lowers the pitch of the instrument.

PHRASING

The breath marks ('), in addition to indicating the proper places to breathe, also serve as an introduction to the feeling of proper phrasing of melodies. This is important, as it is that which gives meaning to music.

FOREWORD TO STUDENTS

EMBOUCHURE

Various ways may be used to help the beginning student produce his first note. The following is one method that has proved successful.

Close the lips and then gradually pull back the corners of the mouth until the lip surfaces are even. (Do not stretch the lips tightly). Take a breath, and, gently blowing, produce a " buzzing " sound. The lips must vibrate in the very centre while producing the " buzz ". When you are able to " buzz " steadily you are ready to place the mouthpiece to the lips.

It is considered good practice to place the mouthpiece half on the upper lip and half on the lower lip in the centre of the mouth. (See pictures). An abnormal mouth formation or tooth structure may necessitate modifications of the above, but in general, it is good to strive to form the embouchure as closely as possible like the above.

The tip of the tongue is placed behind the upper teeth, and when ready to produce a tone, jerk the tongue downwards by using the syllable " TU ". The tongue must be moved very quickly. Breath should be taken through the corners of the mouth. DO NOT PUFF OUT YOUR CHEEKS. Practise in front of a mirror.

CORRECT POSITION (POSTURE)

When playing a trombone or euphonium always stand or sit erect with the head up. The trombone should be held as nearly horizontal as possible, with the arms slightly away from the body. (Fig. 1). The correct position for holding the euphonium and proper sitting posture are shown in Fig. 2.

When practising, it is better to play in a standing position as this will help you to breathe properly.

Your teacher will instruct you as to the proper method of holding the instrument.

FINGERING THE VALVES

The first three fingers of the right hand are used to press down the valves. The first finger for the 1st valve (nearest the mouthpiece) marked (1), the second finger, 2nd valve marked (2), the third finger, 3rd valve marked (3). The fourth or little finger should be free to move with the other fingers. The mark (o) indicates an open note and is played without the use of any valves.

TECHNICAL

Fig. I

The most important technical points for wind instrument players are as follows:

(1) Developing and strengthening the lip muscles.
(*Process*) Playing of long sustained notes.

(2) Developing clarity and precision in attack.
(*Process*) Proper use of the tongue.

(3) Developing a fine quality of tone.
(*Process* A combination of No. 1 and careful listening.

(4) Developing fluency in fingering.
(*Process*) Playing of scales and arpeggios in various keys.

(5) Developing a mastery of the entire range of the instrument.
(*Process*) A combination of all of the above.

Fig. II

CARE OF THE INSTRUMENT

Your instrument will not sound its best, nor will your learning to play it be as easy unless everything pertaining to it is kept in perfect condition.

SLIDE-VALVES: Lubricate them with a good grade of slide or valve oil. Occasionally clean the slide or valves with a little paraffin or petrol. Dry thoroughly and use fresh oil. Remove, clean and replace one valve at a time. A few drops of oil on the stocking at the bottom of the slides is sufficient.

TUNING AND VALVE SLIDES: These slides, as well as the valve caps on the Euphonium, should be greased with a little vaseline to keep them free. Try them twice a week.

MOUTHPIECE AND TUBING: Unless you clean the inside of your instrument, a coating of saliva will form which will greatly interfere with its playing qualities. At least once a week run lukewarm soap suds through your instrument. Be sure to rinse with clear warm water. Take pride in the way your instrument looks by keeping it bright and clean. Be sure to remove mouthpiece after playing.

FAILURE ON YOUR PART IN NOT FOLLOWING OUT REGULARLY THE ABOVE INSTRUCTIONS, IN REGARD TO THE CARE OF YOUR INSTRUMENT WILL RESULT IN EXPENSIVE REPAIR COSTS.

Reference Position and Fingering Chart
for
*Trombone or Euphonium (Baritone)

The Trombone and Euphonium are pitched in B flat.   The following succession of notes in this key are given for quick reference.

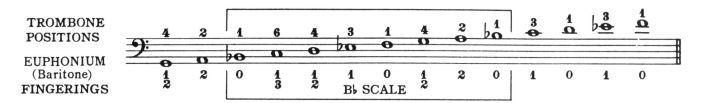

Enharmonic notes: Notes that sound the same, and for which the same positions and valve fingerings are used, but which are written differently are called enharmonic notes. Those most frequently used are the following:

TRB.	5		3		1		5		3		5	
EUPH.	F# or Gb $\binom{2}{3}$		G# or Ab (1)		A# or Bb (0)		C# or Db $\binom{2}{3}$		D# or Eb (1)		F# or Gb $\binom{2}{3}$	

TRB.	3		1		4		2		3		5	
EUPH.	G# or Ab (1)		A# or Bb (0)		Bb or Cb $\binom{1}{2}$		C# or Db (2)		D# or Eb (1)		F# or Gb $\binom{2}{3}$	

Notice that there are seven positions for the Trombone and seven combinations of valve fingerings for the Euphonium. Notes marked (x) are playable but slightly out of tune.

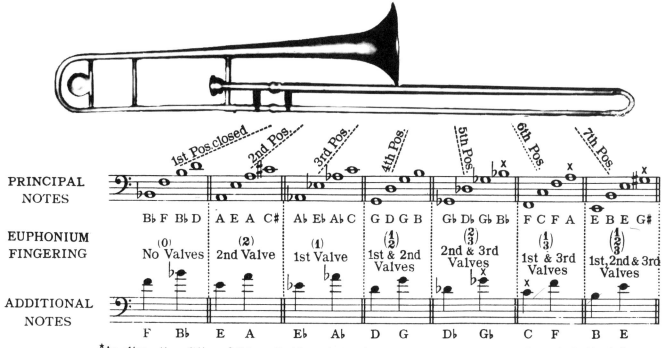

	1st Pos. closed	2nd Pos.	3rd Pos.	4th Pos.	5th Pos.	6th Pos.	7th Pos.
EUPHONIUM FINGERING	Bb F Bb D (0) No Valves	A E A C# (2) 2nd Valve	Ab Eb Ab C (1) 1st Valve	G D G B $\binom{1}{2}$ 1st & 2nd Valves	Gb Db Gb Bb $\binom{2}{3}$ 2nd & 3rd Valves	F C F A $\binom{1}{3}$ 1st & 3rd Valves	E B E G# $\binom{1}{2}{3}$ 1st, 2nd & 3rd Valves
ADDITIONAL NOTES	F Bb	E A	Eb Ab	D G	Db Gb	C F	B E

*An alternative edition of this method is published for students who prefer reading from the treble clef.

A TUNE A DAY

LESSON 1

OBJECTIVES: 1. To learn the correct habits of
    (a) Holding the trombone or euphonium (baritone.)
    (b) Position of mouthpiece.
    (c) Breathing and production of tone.
2. To correlate the positions on the trombone or the valves of the euphonium with the notes on the staff. F-E♭.
3. To know the value of minims, crotchets and their equivalent rests.
4. To know the meaning of the repeat sign.

Preparation: 3 open notes, slide closed, 1st position (no valves)

MINIMS (2 Count) Notes   and MINIM (2 Count) Rests

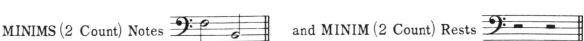

EUPHONIUM FINGERING IS INDICATED BY FIGURES IN PARENTHESES (0)

Introducing 4th line F   Played in the 1st position. (Slide closed / No valves)

This note is F and is played in the 1st position (open / no valves)

① Think Count: 1 2 3 4   REPEAT

This note is ____ and is played in the ____ position with the ____ valves

② Think Count: 1 2 3 4

CROTCHETS (1 Count) Notes   and CROTCHET (1 Count) Rests

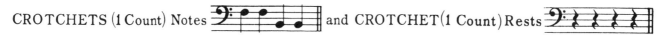

③ Think Count: 1 2 3 4

These are _____ and receive ____ count?

④ Think Count: 1 2 3 4   1 2 3 4

Copyright 1944, by The Boston Music Co.

Minims and Crotchets

Home work: Write a line of crotchets and minims using E♭ and F. Mark the letter name below and the position used for each note.

Advanced students may also play the teacher parts in all lessons.   ** Not in the Cornet book.

LESSON 2

OBJECTIVES: 1. Continuation of the objectives of lesson 1.
2. Learning the names, positions or fingerings of the new notes D-C-B♭
3. Learn the meaning of the breath mark (')

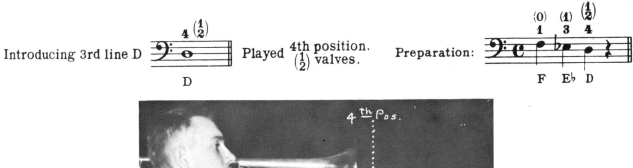

Introducing 3rd line D   Played 4th position. (½) valves.   Preparation:

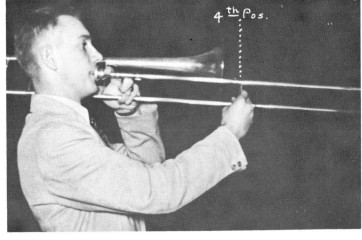

4ᵗʰ Pos.

This note is D and is played in the 4th position with the (½) valves.

① Think Count: 1   2   3   4

These are_____ and receive_____ count.

② Think Count: 1 2 3 4

This note is_____ and is played_____ position. valves.

③ Think Count: 1   2   3   4

These are_____ and receive_____ count.

④ Think Count: 1   2   3   4

This note is_____   **Melody**   This note is_____

⑤ Think Count: 1 2 3 4

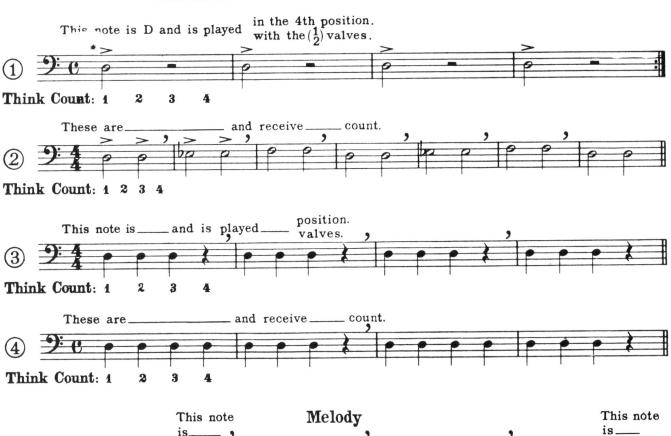

*Attack each note firmly (>)

LESSON 2A

Introducing 2nd space C  Played 6 th position. $\binom{1}{3}$ valves. Preparation

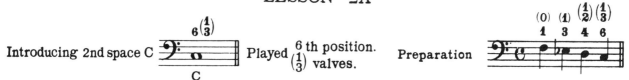

This note is C and is played in the 6th position. with the $\binom{1}{3}$ valves.

⑥

Think Count: 1 2 3 4

These are_____ and receive_____ counts.

⑦

Think Count: 1 2 3 4

This note is_____ and is played_____ position. valves.

⑧

Think Count: 1 2 3 4

These are_____ and receive_____ counts.

⑨

Think Count: 1 2 3 4

Melody

⑩

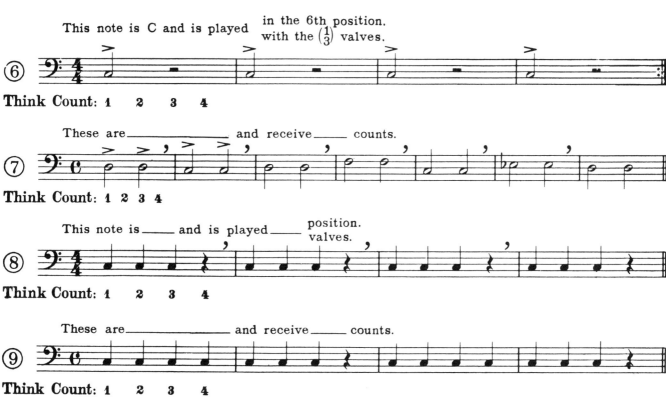

LESSON 2B

Introducing 2nd line B flat 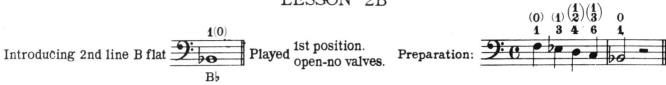 Played 1st position. open-no valves. Preparation:

Bb

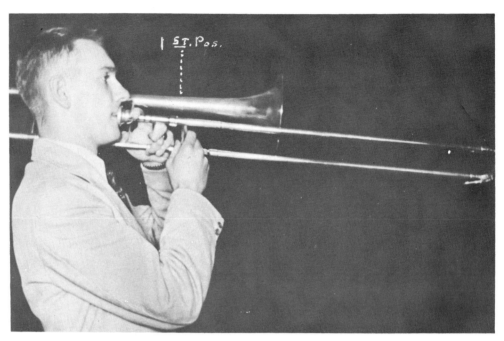

This note is Bb and is played 1st position. (0) no valves.

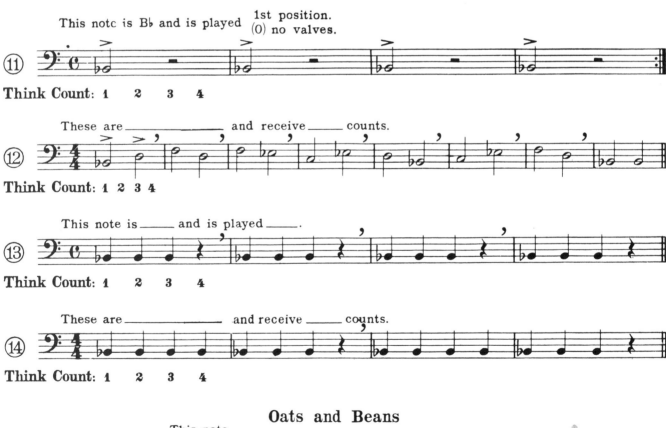

⑪

Think Count: 1   2   3   4

These are _____ and receive _____ counts.

⑫

Think Count: 1 2 3 4

This note is _____ and is played _____.

⑬

Think Count: 1   2   3   4

These are _____ and receive _____ counts.

⑭

Think Count: 1   2   3   4

Oats and Beans

This note is _____

⑮

Think Count: 1 2 3 4

WRITE IN
NOTE NAMES ON
AND SLIDES! X

LESSON 3

OBJECTIVES: 1. Learn the meaning of the TIE.
2. Application of acquired knowledge in playing familiar melodies.

Tied Notes

When two notes on the same line or space of the staff are tied by a slur ⌒, they are to be played as one note, adding the value of the two notes together.

Home work: Mark the fingering (positions) above, and the letter names below all notes in exercises 3, 4, 5 and 6.
Write line of notes thus far studied. Divide into bars using minims and crotchets.
*To continue as before.

8

LESSON 4

OBJECTIVES: 1. Learn the value of a semibreve.
2. Comparison of different note values.
3. Playing easy duets (both parts).

These are _____ and receive _____ counts.

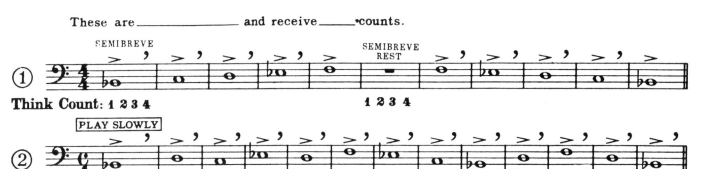

Think Count: 1 2 3 4   1 2 3 4

Different Note Values

It is not necessary to play exercise 3 in the order written. Start at the different letters so as to be able to hear and sound any note.

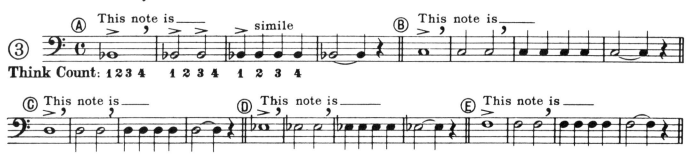

Think Count: 1 2 3 4   1 2 3 4   1 2 3 4

Duet (Two Parts)

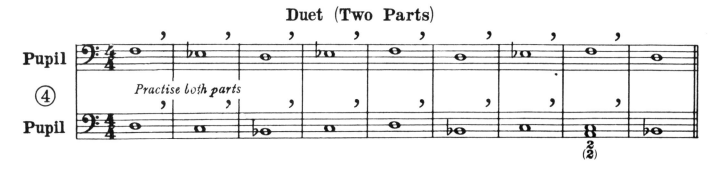

Trio (Three Parts)

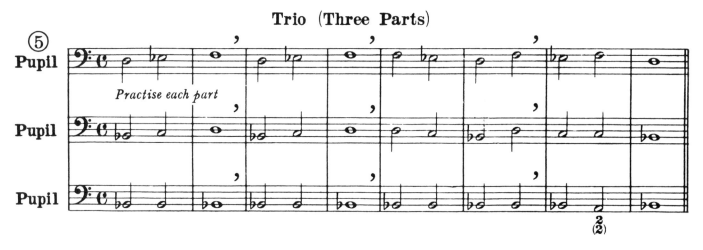

LESSON 5

OBJECTIVES: 1. Learning the name, position or fingering
for fourth space (G).
2. Emphasis on rhythm (note values).

Introducing 4th space G

Played 4th position valves

Preparation:

Little F and G March

Melody

Folk Song

Twinkle, Twinkle, Little Star

Unfamiliar Melody — Test   The Boat Song

Think (position / fingering) and values.

C. P. H.
MINIM REST

Home work: You can't be too familiar with the names of notes and how to play them so if you wish to learn, mark this lesson as before.

LESSON 6

OBJECTIVES: 1. Learning the meaning of the ♮ (natural)
2. Learning the name, position or fingering for 3rd space E♮.
3. Learn the meaning of an accidental.
4. Application of acquired knowledge by playing familiar melodies.

Introducing 3rd space E natural (E♮)   Played 2nd position. 2nd valve.

A NATURAL SIGN (♮) TAKES AWAY THE EFFECT OF A SHARP (♯) OR FLAT (♭).

ACCIDENTALS ARE SHARPS AND FLATS WHICH DO NOT BELONG TO THE KEY SIGNATURE, OR ANY NATURALS, DOUBLE-SHARPS AND DOUBLE-FLATS THAT MAY BE ENCOUNTERED.

Home work: Mark the position or fingering above, and the name below all notes in Ex. 4, 5 and 6.

OBJECTIVES: 1.   Learn the meaning of key signatures.
2.   Learn the key of B♭ major (B♭ and E♭), of C major (no sharps or flats).
3.   Application of acquired knowledge in playing DUETS.
4.   Learning to hear intervals (difference in pitch between two notes).

Key Signatures

The sharps or flats found after the Clef at the beginning of each line is called the Key Signature. These Sharps or Flats affect all the notes of the same name throughout the piece, except when changed by a new Key signature or temporarily by an accidental.

THE KEY OF C HAS NO SHARPS OR FLATS. EX. 2 and 3. THE KEY OF B♭ HAS 2 FLATS (B♭ and E♭). EX. 1 and 4. ALWAYS THINK THE SHARPS OR FLATS AS INDICATED IN THE KEY SIGNATURE.

Duets   (Practise Both Parts)

Upidee   Key of B♭—Two flats (B♭ & E♭)

Upidee   Key of C — No sharps (♯) or flats (♭)

Merrily   (Key of ___)

Au clair de la lune   (Key of ___ the flats are ___)

LESSON 8

OBJECTIVES: 1. Learning the name, position or fingering for fifth line A flat.
2. Learn the meaning of a flat (♭).
3. Learning the proper use of the lip muscles to produce the higher notes.
4. Learning the key of E♭. Three flats (B♭-E♭-A♭).
5. To recognize and know the meaning of the up beat.

Introducing top line A flat   Played 3rd position.
1st valve.

A FLAT (♭) LOWERS THE NOTE TO WHICH IT APPLIES BY ONE SEMITONE.

BEFORE NAMING OR PLAYING ANY NOTE BE SURE TO NOTICE THE KEY SIGNATURE.

Key of E♭, (B♭-E♭-A♭). These flats placed just after the clef sign, mean that every B-E & A will be played flat, except when cancelled by a natural (♮). Ex. 5, E♮.

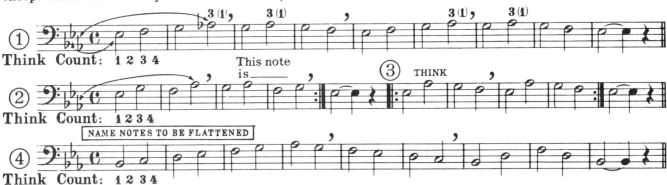

Many pieces begin with an incomplete bar, usually starting with the last beat or fraction thereof. This is called the up-beat. The ending always completes the bar of the up-beat.

An accidental is a sharp or flat which does not belong to the key signature. An accidental applies only to the bar in which it is placed. Ex. 5, E♮

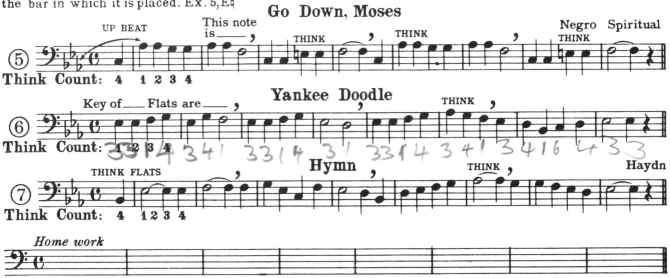

Home work

Home work: Write line of notes thus far studied, using semibreves, minims and crotchets. Mark fingering **above and** letter names below.

OBJECTIVES: 1. Learning the name, position or fingering for
fifth line A (natural).
2. Continued emphasis on rhythm and fingering.
3. Learning the key of F (one flat) and of C (no flats).

Introducing top line A natural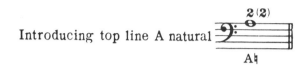

Played 2nd position.
2nd valve.

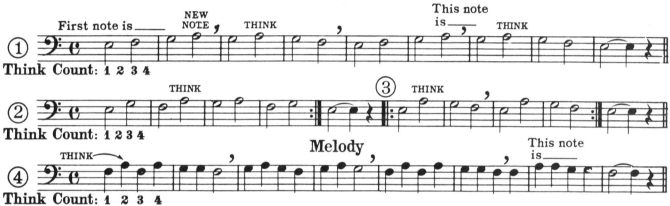

KEY OF F-ONE FLAT (B♭) MEANS TO FLAT EVERY B UNLESS CANCELLED BY A NATURAL SIGN (♮).

*Teacher: Write line of notes used through this lesson as a sight reading test.
Use key signature and accidentals.

LESSON 10

OBJECTIVES: 1. Learning the name, position or fingering for one space above the staff (Bb).
2. To know the formation of the natural scale, (Placement of tones and semitones).
3. Playing the Bb scale and arpeggio from memory. (Ex. 8 and 9)

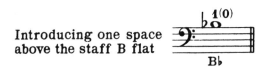

Introducing one space above the staff B flat

Played 1st position.
no valves.

Think Count: 1 2 3 4

Think Count: 1 2 3 4

The Scale

A scale is a succession of notes from a given note (key note) to its octave, 8 notes higher. The form on which all major scale are modelled is as follows:

The Natural, or Bb Major Scale for the trombone

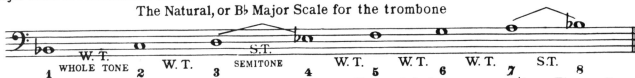

The ascending progression is: two whole tones, one semitone, three whole tones, one semitone. The semitones come between the numbers 3-4 and 7-8.

Bb Major Scale
(Bb and Eb)

Bb Major Arpeggio (Broken Chord)

Ruben and Rachel

Home work

*Not in Cornet book.
Home work: Write the Bb major scale. Use key signature and place flats before notes affected.

Slurred Notes (legato)*
For trombone only

OBJECTIVE: Application of proper use of lip muscles to
play slurred *(legato)* notes.

There are two kinds of slurred notes, i. e. *Lip* or *Natural* slurs (notes played with the same slide position or valves) (see page 32) and legato slurs **(notes** played with a change in slide position). Euphonium
players are not affected by this latter type of articulation.

Legato slurs are difficult to execute, but when mastered are extremely effective.

In order to avoid the "smear" which is caused by the movement of the slide from one position to another,
the tongue must be used for practically every note in order to change positions more smoothly. By using
the syllable "Tu" on the first of a group of legato notes and the syllable "Du" on the remaining notes, a
smooth carrying over of the sound of each note will result. Each note must literally "melt" into the next
tone. This is the meaning of legato.

TEACHER:

In order to parallel the cornet book in succeeding lessons, this page is introduced earlier than is ordinarily
the case.

The above exercise should be repeated using other notes and positions.

Changing of one slide position.

Skips of more than one slide position are more difficult to play smoothly, but are executed in the same
manner as the above.

*This sign (⌢ slur) when placed above or below two or more notes indicates that they are to be played
smoothly and connected *(legato)*.

LESSON 11

OBJECTIVES: 1. The use of slurred notes in familiar melodies.
2. To learn the value of the quaver.
3. Rhythms involving quavers in $\frac{4}{4}$ and $\frac{2}{4}$ time.
4. Correlation of notes thus far studied (name and position on the staff) with proper position or fingering.

Hymn

Lightly Row

Quavers

A quaver ♪ is equal to $\frac{1}{2}$ of a crotchet and receives $\frac{1}{2}$ of a count in $\frac{4}{4}$ or $\frac{2}{4}$ time. Two quavers (♫) equal one crotchet or one count, four quavers equal one minim (2 counts) and eight quavers equal one semibreve (4 counts). A quaver rest (𝄾) is equal to the value of a quaver.

BE SURE TO LEARN THE RHYTHM DRILLS THOROUGHLY (learn to feel the division of the beats) BEFORE PLAYING THE MELODIES. THIS IS IMPORTANT.

Comparison of $\frac{4}{4}$ with $\frac{2}{4}$ Time

One bar of $\frac{4}{4}$ time equals two bars of $\frac{2}{4}$ time.

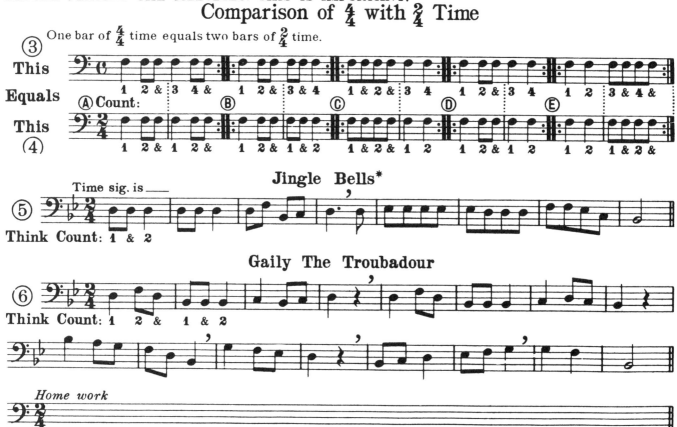

Jingle Bells*

Gaily The Troubadour

*Not in Cornet book.

Home work: Write line of notes thus far studied, using minims, crotchets and quavers in $\frac{2}{4}$ time.

OBJECTIVES: 1. **Learning new rhythm**—¾ time—with emphasis
on rhythm drills. (A-B-C etc.)
2. **Use of dotted** crotchets and quavers. (Ex. F)
3. **The application** of acquired knowledge.

The Dotted Minim and the Dotted Crotchet

A dot is equal to one half the value of the note it follows. A dotted minim equals 3 beats, a dotted crotchet equals 1½ beats.

Rhythm Drills

DRILL: Count aloud each variation, A-B-C etc. while clapping the hands once for each note until the rhythms are felt and memorized, then try to play them using any single note. When this can be done freely, play the exercises as written. REMEMBER—Rhythm must be felt before it can be played.

Combination of Rhythms in ¾ time

Think Count: REST

Home work

Home work: Write 8 bars of notes thus far studied, using different groupings **of notes in** ¾ time. **Mark** positions (valves) **and note names as before.**

LESSON 13

[Continuation of Dotted Minims and Dotted Crotchets in ¾ and ²⁄₄ Time]

OBJECTIVES: 1. Application of ¾ and ²⁄₄ rhythms in familiar
melodies of different keys.
2. Knowledge of the first and second time bars.
3. Learning to play melodies from memory.
4. Application of slurs and key changes.
5. Knowledge of terms used for tempo (speed).

Home work: Learn to play one of the above melodies from memory.

OBJECTIVES: 1. Application of acquired knowledge.
2. Carols for recreation.
3. Knowledge of the fermata ⌒ (pause)

We Three Kings of Orient Are

* ⌒ Pause (fermata) A short curved line drawn over a dot, prolongs the time of the note.
Home work: Learn to play from memory the above melodies.

LESSON 15

OBJECTIVES: 1. Learning the name, position or fingering of one line
above the staff C.
2. Memorizing The National Anthem
3. Application of acquired knowledge in varied keys and
rhythms.

Introducing one line above the staff C   Played 3rd position 1st valve

Home work

Home work: Write line of notes thus far studied, using different note values. Mark positions (valves) **above** and letter name below.

OBJECTIVES: 1. Learning the name, position or fingering for low A♮.
2. Learning the proper use of the lip muscles to produce the lower notes.
3. Knowledge of key and rhythm changes.
4. The playing of quavers in a faster tempo. (Ex. 5)
5. The playing of two quavers on the up-beat. (Ex. 4)

Introducing low A♮   Played 2nd position. 2nd valve.

Home work: Write line of notes in 2/4 time, using new note in this lesson and mark as before, also write line in 3/4 time. Use different valued notes thus far studied.

LESSON 17

Duets

OBJECTIVES: 1. Ability to play independent secondary parts where the note values are not the same as in the first part.
2. Application of acquired knowledge of slurs and accidentals.

American Hymn

LESSON 18

OBJECTIVES: 1. Learning the name, position or fingering for second space
above the staff D.
2. Application of proper use of lip muscles to produce
higher notes.
3. Application of all subject-matter learned thus far.

Introducing high D **9:** Played 1st position
no valves (open)

Home work: Write line of notes, using the new note in this lesson. Mark as before.
Mark exercise 4 the same way.

LIP SLURS

OBJECTIVE: Application of proper use of lip muscles
to play lip slurs.

Listen carefully to the intonation in the examples below. Some positions have to be altered slightly to play the notes in tune. Your ear should tell you.

Army bugle calls are written on four notes and may be played with any of the following positions or valve combinations.

Pos.	1	2	3	4	5	6	7
Valves	0	(2)	1)	$(\frac{1}{2})$	$(\frac{2}{3})$	$(\frac{1}{3})$	$(\frac{1}{2}\frac{1}{3})$

OBJECTIVES: 1. Learning the name, position or fingering for low Ab.
2. Knowledge of the key of Ab (Bb-Eb-Ab-Db)
3. Application of acquired knowledge through the playing of familiar and unfamiliar melodies.
4. Learn position or fingering of low G. (Ex. 6, lower part)

Introducing low Ab   Played   3rd position   1st valve

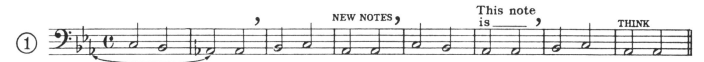

Key of Ab, 4 flats, Bb, Eb, Ab & Db. These flats, placed at the beginning of each staff, mean flatten every B, E, A & D, except when cancelled by a natural (♮). (See lesson 21)

Merrily

Familiar Melodies (*Listen carefully*)

French Folk Song

Harvest Time

Unfamiliar Melody—Test

C. P. H.

Duet

Andante

von Weber

LESSON 20*

(Intermediate notes—Chromatics)

OBJECTIVES: 1. Understanding and playing chromatics
2. Knowledge of enharmonic notes.
3. Learning new fingerings.

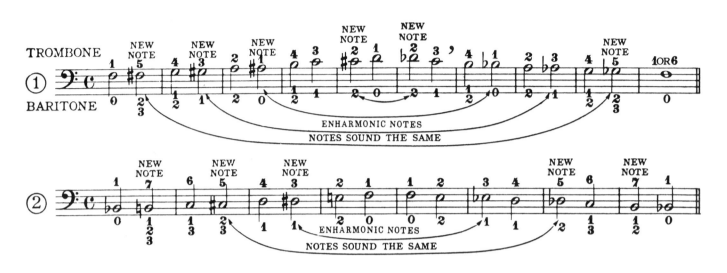

Chromatic Scales

The word "chromatic" means moving by semitones. A chromatic scale is one that ascends or descends by half steps.

Chromatic Waltz

C. P. H.

*This lesson cannot be played with the Cornets.

LESSON 21
Melodies in the Keys of C & A♭

Scale of C Major
(No Sharps or Flats)

Home work:

Home work: **Play from memory the scales of the keys used in this lesson.**

LESSON 22

OBJECTIVES: 1. Learning a new rhythm.
2. Understanding Alla breve (cut time) ($\frac{2}{2}$ time)

Alla Breve or $\frac{2}{2}$ Time

Alla Breve, or cut time ₵ is played the same as $\frac{2}{4}$ time. Each note having half the value as in $\frac{4}{4}$ time, a minim being the unit of a beat.

Rhythm Drills

Drill: Count aloud each pattern while clapping the hands once for each note.
REMEMBER—Unless you feel a rhythm you cannot play it.
Play the B♭ scale, using these patterns until the rhythms are memorized.

There's Music in the Air

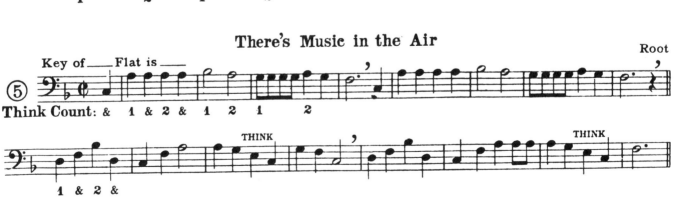

OBJECTIVES: 1. Continuation of Alla breve (cut time).
2. The playing of a full length march.
3. Application of acquired knowledge.
4. Knowledge of the meaning of this sign (∕).
5. Knowledge of signs indicating volume of tone (dynamics).

Advancement March*

In March time (alla marcia)

C. P. H.

*All marches generally consist of an introduction, 1st and 2nd strain, each repeated, followed by a Trio. The key of the Trio is always a fifth lower than that of the first part.
**This sign ∕ means to repeat the preceding bar.

Syncopation**

Syncopation is an artificial accent, an interruption of the natural pulsation of the music. It can be produced by giving an accent where none is expected, or by taking away the accent from the point where it is expected. Accents should be quite strong in syncopation. Another method of producing syncopation is the tying of the last note of one bar to the first note of the next.

Same as above but in Cut time (Alla breve)

Our Boys will Shine

Czech Folk Song

*Accent Attack these notes a little stronger than the others.
**This lesson is not in the Cornet book.

LESSON 24

OBJECTIVES: 1. Learning another new rhythm.
2. Knowledge and use of the rhythm of $\frac{6}{8}$ time.
3. Counting 6 to a bar and 2 to a bar.
4. Application of new rhythm in familiar melodies.

Row, Row, Row Your Boat

Oats and Beans

Mulberry Bush

Home work

Home work: Write line of notes, using different rhythm patterns in $\frac{6}{8}$ time.

LESSON 25

OBJECTIVES: 1. Continuation of six-eight time. (slow)
2. Counting six beats to a bar.
3. Application of acquired knowledge in familiar tunes.
4. Playing of duet in six-eight time.

It Came Upon a Midnight Clear

Drink to Me Only With Thine Eyes

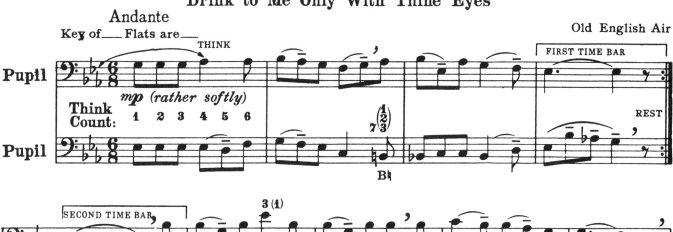

*rit., abbreviation of ritenuto — gradually slower in speed.

LESSON 26

OBJECTIVES: 1. Continuation of six-eight time. (fast)
2. Counting two beats to a bar. (march time)
3. Application of acquired knowledge in familiar tunes.
4. Playing a march in six-eight time.

Skipping Along

With spirit (Allegro)

C.P.H.

*Not in the Cornet book

LESSON 27

OBJECTIVES: Learning the use of semiquavers.
        (a) Equivalents
        (b) Counting semiquavers.

Semiquavers

A semiquaver  is equal to half the value of a quaver

Two semiquavers equal one quaver 🎵=🎵 and four semiquavers equal one crotchet 🎵=🎵

Abbreviations for semiquavers.

Comparative table showing number of semiquavers to other notes studied thus far.

① Note time signatures
1 & 2 & & &

② Note time signatures
1 & & 2 & &

③ Note time signatures   ④
1 & & 2 & &   1 & & & 2 &

Mac Donald's Farm

Key of ____ Flats are ____   THINK

This note is ____

Home work

Home work: Write line of notes, using different groupings of semiquavers in ²₄ time.

Supplementary Material using Semiquavers*

Camptown Races

Stephen Foster

Russian Folk Song

Triplets

Triplets are groups of three notes played in the time of two notes of the same value. They are indicated by a figure ⌢3 and a slur placed over or under a group of three notes.

A bar of 2/4 containing two triplets 2/4 ♪♪♪♪♪♪ is the same as a bar of 6/8 in march time. 6/8 ♪♪♪♪♪♪

Pilgrims' Chorus

(Tannhäuser)

Richard Wagner

Theme from Bohemian Girl

Balfe

*This lesson is not in Cornet book.

LESSON 28

OBJECTIVES: 1. Dotted quavers and semiquavers, legato.
2. Correct division of each beat.
3. Application of new rhythm.

Dotted Quavers and Semiquavers
Legato (Connected)

This is one of the more difficult rhythms to learn. The dotted quaver is equal to three semiquavers. Always feel a division of four on one beat when playing this rhythm, three on the dotted quaver and one on the semiquaver.

BE SURE TO PLAY THE DOTTED QUAVERS LONG ENOUGH AND THE SEMIQUAVERS SHORT ENOUGH.

Largo
(New World Symphony)
Duet

Dvořák

Very slow (Largo)

Home work

Home work: Write line of notes, using dotted quavers and semiquavers.
cresc. — Gradually louder.

OBJECTIVES: 1. Dotted quavers and semiquavers, staccato. (detached)
2. Application of this difficult rhythm in familiar melodies using $\frac{2}{4}$ and $\frac{4}{4}$ time.

Dotted Quavers and Semiquavers
Staccato (Detached)

Dotted quavers and semiquavers played staccato (detached) are separated by a short pause as follows:

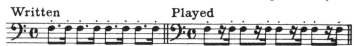

Joy to the World
(Duet)

Handel

Battle Hymn of the Republic

Steffe

LESSON 30

OBJECTIVE: Continued application of dotted quavers and semiquavers $\frac{3}{4}$ and $\frac{6}{8}$ time.

Maryland, My Maryland
(Duet)

Silent Night, Holy Night
(Duet)

Gruber

LESSON 31

OBJECTIVES: 1. Learning the name, position or fingering for high E♭ and E♮.
2. Playing the scale of E♭ major from memory.
3. Using new notes in familiar melodies.

Home work: Write E♭ major scale. Use key signature and place flats before the notes affected. Learn to play this scale from memory.

LESSON 32

OBJECTIVES: 1. Learning the name, position or fingering for high **F**.
                    2. Playing the scale of F major from memory.
                    3. Learning variations to Ex. 5.

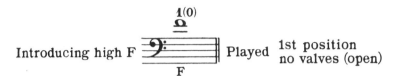

Introducing high F   Played   1st position
                                           no valves (open)

Scale and Arpeggio in F Major

Recite scale before playing.

Scale Study

Key of____Play slowly at first

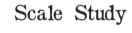

Old Russian Hymn

Lento (Slowly)

Home work

Home work: Write the F major scale. Use key signature and place flat before notes affected. **Learn to play this scale from memory.**

Table of Harmonics for Tenor Trombone

Prepared by W. J. Duthoit

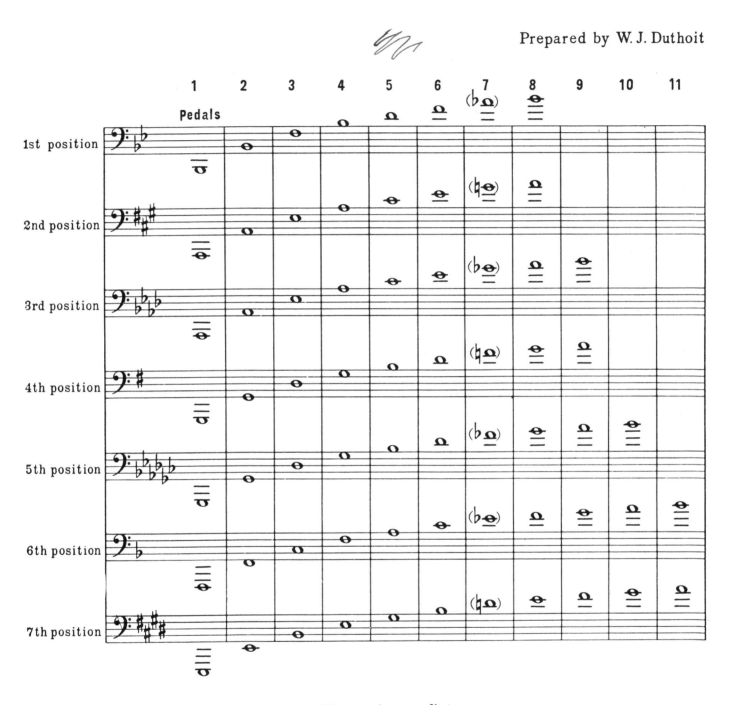

N.B.   7th Harmonics are flat

11th Harmonics are sharp

Table of Harmonics for Euphonium 𝄢 (Baritone)

Prepared by W. J. Duthoit

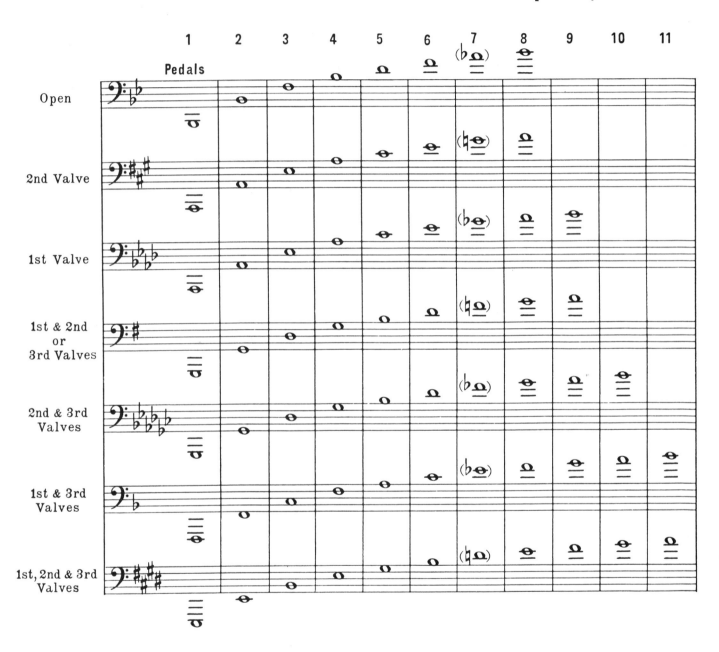

N.B. 7th Harmonics are flat

11th Harmonics are sharp

Printed in England by Commercial Colour Press Plc, 11/01 (42109)